Billy the Kid

I can read the Speed sounds.

I can read the Green words.

I can read the Red words.

I can read the story.

I can answer the questions about the story.

I can read the Speed words.

Say the Speed sounds

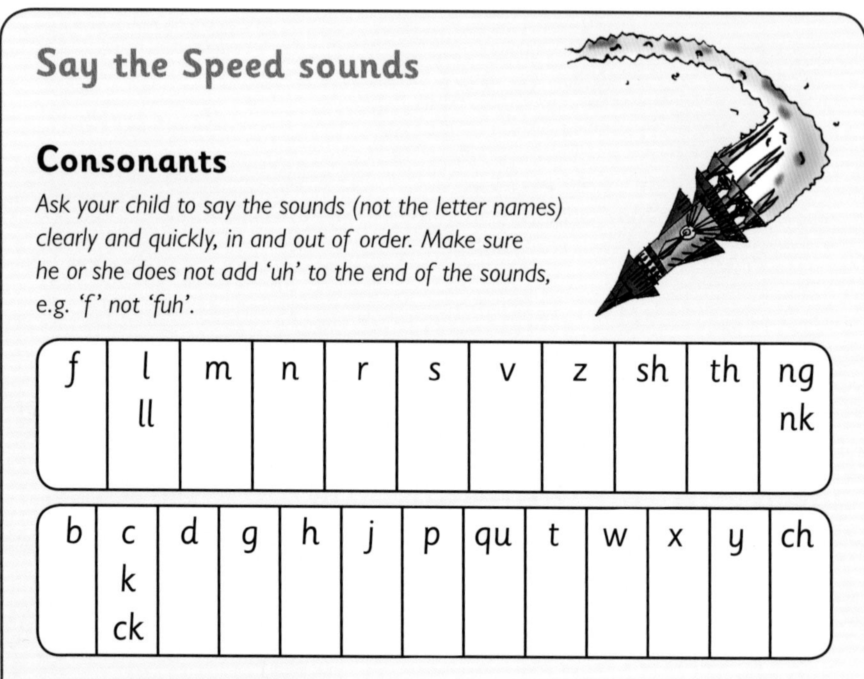

Consonants

Ask your child to say the sounds (not the letter names) clearly and quickly, in and out of order. Make sure he or she does not add 'uh' to the end of the sounds, e.g. 'f' not 'fuh'.

f	l ll	m	n	r	s	v	z	sh	th	ng nk

b	c k ck	d	g	h	j	p	qu	t	w	x	y	ch

Each box contains one sound.

Vowels

Ask your child to say each vowel sound and then the word, e.g. 'a', 'at'.

at	hen	in	on	up	day	see	high	blow	zoo

Read the Green words

For each word ask your child to read the separate sounds, e.g. 'r-e-d', 'w-i-ll' and then blend the sounds together to make the word, e.g. 'red', 'will'. Sometimes one sound is represented by more than one letter, e.g. 'th', 'll', 'ou'. These are underlined.

troll will bad big yum

get red plum kid and

fat trip trap his pond

trot

Read the Red words

Red words don't sound like they look. Read the words out to your child. Explain that he or she will have to stop and think about how to say the red words in the story.

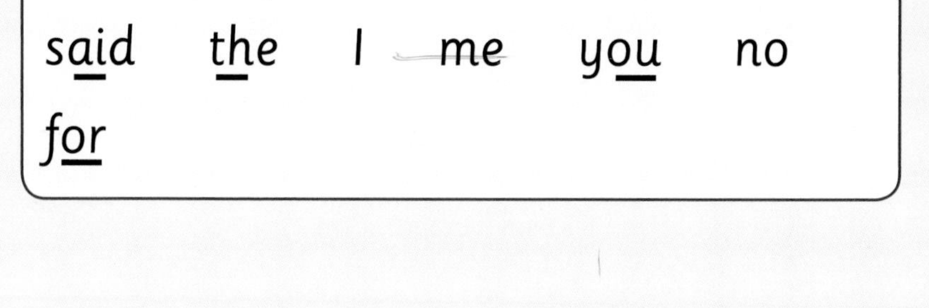

said the I me you no

for

Billy the Kid

Introduction
This is a story about the three billy goats (Mum, Dad and Billy the Kid) who want to cross a bridge, but are stopped by a troll.

Billy the Kid, his mum and his dad.

Trot, trot. Trot, trot.

“Let me get a fat red plum. A fat red plum will fill me up,” said Billy the Kid.

“Yes!” said Mum and Dad.

“Yum, yum!”

Stop! Stop!

A big, bad troll.

"Troll! Troll! Let me cross,"
said Billy the Kid.
"Let me get a fat red plum."

"No," said the big
bad troll.

"Mum," said Billy the Kid. "The troll is big. The troll is bad. Get me a plum."

"Troll! Troll! Let me cross,"
said Mum.
"Let me get a fat red plum."

"No," said the big bad troll.

"Dad," said Mum.
"The troll is big. The troll is bad.
Get Billy the Kid a fat red plum."

“Troll! Troll! Let me cross,” said Dad.
“Let me get a fat red plum.”

"No," said the big bad troll.

Dad said, “Then I will put you in the pond!”

Splash!

“Help! Help!”

Dad can cross.
Trip, trap.

Mum and Billy the Kid
can cross.
Trip, trap. Trip, trap.

A plum for Dad,
a plum for Mum
and a plum for Billy the Kid.

"Yum, yum!"

But no plum for the big wet troll.

"Sob! Sob!"

Questions to talk about

Ask your child:

Page 8: *Who are the characters in this story?*

Page 10: *Why does Billy the Kid want to cross the bridge?*
Why do you think the troll says no?

Page 17: *What does Dad say he will do to the troll?*
How do you think the troll is feeling now?
(furious, frustrated, mad)

Page 19: *What are the goats thinking now?*

Speed words

Ask your child to read the words across the rows, down the columns and in and out of order, clearly and quickly.

troll	bad	let	big	yum
get	red	plum	kid	Mum
and	will	fat	trip	trap
Dad	said	me	you	pond